Behind the Cuts

Megan Marie

For information: meganmarievd@gmail.com

ISBN
9798632668941

Cover by Barbara Gottlieb
www.gottgraphix.com

Self-Published with
Ronni Sanlo Consulting
www.ronnisanlo.com
Sequim, WA 98382

Printed in the United States of America

DEDICATION

To my two favorite professors who made a deep impact on me. Stacie Bell's mentorship and teaching guided me forward. Dr. Alan Lapin once told me, "We have stories to write." Hearing that helped me move forward with this book. Going to college and writing this book have been dreams come true. And to the many therapists and friendships I've made along the way.

Namaste
Megan

iv

ACKNOWLEDGEMENTS

This has been a long, slow journey. First and foremost, I wish to acknowledge the many therapists and support people who guided me along the way even when I was unable to guide myself.

I also acknowledge Dr. Ronni Sanlo and Dr. Kelly Watson for their time, editing and encouragement.

Finally, I am deeply grateful that my family came back to life.

Megan Marie
2020

FOREWORD

This book is a young woman's story about her desire to stop cutting. Cutting, often called self-injury or self-harming, stems from a dysfunctional attempt to regulate emotions. It is an intentional way to relieve tension and to cope with emotional pain, intense anger and frustration. Although self-harming behavior is well understood by professionals, it can still be alarming to both the person who self-harms and to their family members and friends.

Most people who self-harm are teenagers and young adults, though similar behavior may be found in other age groups as well.

Preventing or stopping self-harming behaviors are challenging. Dr. Trevor Buser, an assistant professor of counseling at Rider University in New Jersey said, "Training in stress management techniques, such as mindfulness, diaphragmatic breathing or progressive muscle relaxation, may provide healthy alternatives for individuals who would otherwise perform non-suicidal self-injury for emotional regulation." These same techniques are often coupled with 12-step programs for substance and alcohol abuse as well.

Professional understanding about self-harming has evolved over the past twenty years. Prior to the 1990s, self-mutilation was often known as a failed suicide attempt. This is no longer accepted. As of 2004, self-mutilation has been recognized by the American Psychiatric Association as a feature of other psychiatric disorders. While self-harming behaviors bring a momentary sense of release and calm, it is usually followed by guilt and shame along with the return of unwanted, painful emotions.

Clients present with many different mental health issues. Each is unique with their individual set of challenges and strengths. In this memoir, Megan reminds us that our job as therapists is to be present and to listen. She shares her personal story so that others may understand that healing and recovery from self-harming behaviors are possible.

Perhaps you may relate to Megan's story, or to her parents, or to her therapists. As Megan shares her story, you may be able to feel her hope. Profound healing, knowing that one is not alone, is in full operation throughout this book. Megan graciously and courageously shares her journey from years of self-harm to finding healthier ways to cope with her emotions.

There is no sure way to prevent your loved one's self-harming behaviors. But reducing the risk of self-injury includes strategies that involve both individuals and communities.

I hope this book is helpful for you. Whatever your relationship with people who self-harm might be, may this book encourage you to continue to seek, and to understand.

Dr. Kelly Watson, LISAC

Any Other Way
by Stacy Kuras

She walked to the beat of her own drum
This time, dancing as if there were no others
Not one cross word at her disposal
She was soft to the touch
Beaming from the world around her
Tempted by a fate she could not feel

Standing proud on her own two feet
A glow in her eyes
The best had yet to come
The writing was on the wall
She was down to earth
But definitely not from this earth

No longer afraid of what others might think
Or what they might do to her
She was not scared to say the wrong thing
She was the one
Simply like no other
She was real
She was free
She was whole

And she knew that you knew
So all was well

No longer somebody else's failure
She was finally a trophy worth showing
To live life in her own way
Of her own choosing
On her own terms
In her own time
On her own dime
She simply would not have it
Any other way

Any Other Way © by Stacy Kuras

xii

Chapter 1
Cherry Hall

The glass cuts deep into my skin. I sit here in the bathtub watching my blood run down my skin. All my feelings and connections to the world just disappear. Four little slices on the left wrist. Not sure why the left. Maybe because my dominant hand is right? I don't think about it when I do it. I just do it.

Usually if a person gets cut by accident, they try to stop the blood and put a band-aid on the cut, right? That's the normal thing to do. For me, the more blood I see, the calmer I feel. When I cut, it's like an out-of-body experience.

That's how I ended up here, at Cherry Hall. One of the teachers' aids at school caught me sitting on the bathroom floor with a piece of glass and a bloody wrist. She freaked out and took me to the school counselor's office. Next thing I knew, my parents showed up for an emergency conference. The school staff told my parents that

I was a danger to myself and felt that I needed more treatment than what they can give. It was time, they said, that I got some professional help. They didn't want me to come back to school until I had a note from a doctor saying that I had successfully completed a treatment program for teens who cut.

I'm not sure who was more scared, my mother or the school counselor. Probably the school counselor. Her name was Jody Fay. Jody had spent a lot of time with me. It's funny because up until my sophomore year, the school didn't even know who I was. Now the whole staff knows me. I mean, I guess it's not an everyday occurrence that a student is found in the campus bathroom with bloody cut-up wrists. I truly don't think they knew how to deal with me. It's not like I ever heard other students talking about it.

"I can't believe you're putting the family through this. IS there something we haven't done?" my mother asks as I sit in the back seat on our way to the mental hospital. In the words of Dorothy, *we're off to see the wizard*. I find myself singing that in my head. Makes sense, right? Singing in my head. Oh shit, maybe I *am* crazy. But if you stop to think about it, do crazy people take the time to ask themselves if they are crazy? Maybe there's hope for me after all.

"I hope you don't tell the therapist I'm to blame for this thing you're doing to yourself, Chantel. We've done nothing but the best for you. After all, we just bought that brand new piano for you. *This* is how you thank your father and me?"

I still don't say a word as my father drives and my mother gulps down an iced coffee while she hollers at me. I lean my head up against the backseat window, silent. I don't know how to respond. Amazing. Their daughter's school is sending their kid to a nut house and both my parents are already in complete denial. Blaming me for causing shame and trouble to the family instead of asking me if I'm okay, or even saying *I'm so sorry you're doing to this to yourself.* Maybe that's too much to hope for.

As we drive up to the hospital building, I look out the window and see a butterfly on the side of the car. They say that seeing butterflies is a symbol for a loved one who has passed on to heaven. Maybe it's Grams checking up on me. It seems like ever since my grandma died. My world has gone to hell and I lost the only person who ever believed in me and who was on my side. She always hated my dad. Grams didn't use that word much but she really *hated* my dad. Dad the sperm donor, you know? The male protector of the family. If my mother only knew what was really happening between us.

I can't believe that of all the family members, *I'm* the one who gets chosen to be sent to the nut house.

"Hello, can I help you?" The voice on the intercom next to do the door speaks.

"Yes, I'm here to check my daughter in," my mom says with a shaky voice. My dad walks behind her holding my suitcase.

"Come in, come in. You must be Chantel. We've been waiting for you. Please follow me over here to the room. The admissions team will be here shortly," says the woman as she greets us with a big smile on her face. Her name tag says Jan. She's smiling so I'm betting she's not a patient here. The longer we wait for the team to get here, my heart pounds faster and faster. My dad sits next to me. My mom is next to him. I wonder where my younger sister is.

"Hello, I'm Dr. Mynt. These are some of the nurses on the ward. This is June, and Max. Are you Chantel?" Dr. Mynt asks while shaking my hand. I've not said a word. It feels safer that way, to be seen and not heard.

Watching my parents talk to the doctor about what is going on with me, I feel like a fly on the wall. I mean, it's *my* body. *I'm* the one being checked in here. Wouldn't the doctor want to talk to me? I guess being sixteen years old, I don't really have those rights. At least that's the impression I get. I look around the room. I notice there are a couple of flower pictures on the wall. The paint is yellow. The carpet is green. A couple of spots look like some holes may have been painted over.

My dad signs the paperwork. Both of my parents give me a hug. As I stand there with Nurse June, saying goodbye to my parents after they closed the door to this side, I almost feel relieved. My parents are divorced and I've been living with my mom and sister. My dad has visitation every other weekend so this is the first time in a while that I've spent time with both my parents.

June wears an ID tag around her neck on a Disney lanyard. She uses the name tag to open all the doors. Cherry Hall is a locked facility. My heart's racing a million miles a minute as I listen to June speak.

"Okay sweetie, we have to come over here. Please put your suitcase and jacket in the bucket. You have to have a strip search." Without saying a word, I give her this panicked look like she's crazy, but she doesn't seem to be bothered by my not talking. I learned in health class that there are many different ways to speak without using my voice.

As June is conducting the strip search, I start to panic and hyperventilate. It feels like my world is starting to close in on me. For the first time, I feel scared. There's nothing I can do but feel it.

"Oh, honey, what did those bruises come from?" She sees the huge bruises on the back of my leg.

"I fell off my bike." That is the quickest story I could come up with without getting too many more questions.

"Okay. Well, here are some fresh clean sweats. We'll go in here so you can shower. Every new patient who comes to the ward has to go through this. I'll be waiting for you in here." I step into the shower feeling awkward and full of shame knowing that she saw the bruises. The fact that I can't even shower by myself sucks. I try to pretend that she's not there as I feel the heat from the water coming out of the shower head. I just stand there and let the water flow down my back.

June uses her nametag to open another door. This is a whole other world. The walls are slate gray and the carpet is dark blue. There are different pictures of what looks like artwork from the patients here. It is after 9:30 pm so all the girls are in bed. June tells me that I'll meet the other girls tomorrow.

There are three beds to each room and three wooden desks on the wall across from the beds. I choose the bed closest to the window. That's how my bedroom is set up at home. Except for the bars on the windows. I can see outside here but I have to look through the spaces between the bars to see anything. We're not in Kansas anymore.

Chapter 2
Roommates

"Rise and shine, love. Breakfast is in fifteen minutes." The lady stands at my door holding a clipboard as I roll over. Feels like I just went to sleep five minutes ago.

I walk out of my room in my sweats and a hoody. What I don't like is that the nursing staff took the strings out of my sweatshirt because I guess they think I could hang myself. With them. I'm surprised by all the girls who are lined up against the wall. They stare at me as much as I stare at them. Kind of reminds me of my freshman year when the seniors scoped out the first-year students. The funny thing about status in each grade is we all were freshman at one point and worked our way up.

"Okay, ladies. Ready?" It feels like we are about to go on tour through Disneyland or something. We walk a straight line behind the nurse. Latrel follows behind at the end. Latrel is a big black guy. Strong. He'd have to be to work in a place like this.

The cafeteria is set up like the cafeteria at school. There are workers wearing gloves who dish out the food. We have to tell them what we want. It's not already prepared like at school. So many people have allergies these days. We don't get to use real silverware. We have to use plastic. There is a nurse who sits at the end of each table to keep order and to observe the "food issues" girls, meaning the anorexic and bulimic girls.

Each disease is treated on a different floor, but all are together in the cafeteria. The worse the disease the higher up hospital floor. Since I do this to myself, I'm somewhere in the middle. Not suicidal, well not today, not right now, and not schizophrenic. So I'm in-between floors.

"What are you in for?" one of the girls asks as I play with the eggs on the tray.

"My school put me in here," I reply, stuffing my face.

"My mom did it to me," she said. "The bitch decided I was too complicated and an interference with her dating life so she sent me here. I'm JoAnn. Bipolar. This is Charlotte, Ruby, Julie, Stacie, and Olivia. Keep to yourself and keep your head up. You'll be just fine. And don't let JoAnn scare you." Laughter from all the girls at the table. I'm kind of suspicious now. What have I gotten into?

"Ok, ladies, breakfast over. Please pick up your trays then line up to go back to the unit." I'm not sure if all the people who work here are called nurses. I just assume because I'm in a hospital and they are everywhere. If they have a clipboard or a nametag, I figured they're a worker. The people who aren't workers are patients.

We line up at the door again. I hate the sound of the lock on the big doors. Reminds me of jail even though I haven't been in jail. I visited my cousin there one time. She got messed up on meth but she's been clean for a couple years now.

Walking back to the unit I see a chain link fence from the hallway to the other side of the unit. Like a dog in the kennel. All of us in a straight line again. Follow the leader. I finally feel the breeze from the outside for just a minute. I'm quickly reminded by the door buzzer that I'm not outside, just inside a fence.

On my desk there's this blue peachy folder with rules and a schedule. Looks like it's shower time and then morning check-in group.

A lady with the clipboard says, "Good morning girls. Hope everyone's night went well. We'll do check-ins in a minute, but we have someone new joining us. Chantel, would you like to introduce yourself?" Everyone's sitting in a circle. There are ten girls and a group leader.

12

Most of us are wearing some form of sweatpants and a comfy shirt, and most are wearing sandals or flip flops. Tennis shoes are considered a danger because of the laces but who wants to wear a pair of tennis shoes after the laces are gone?

"Who wants to talk first?" the clipboard lady asks and grabs a pen. "Not everybody at once."

"My mom came to visit on visitors' day," Lacey says as she brings her leg up to her chest and rests her chin on her knee. Body language says a lot in here as I sit in the chair closest to the door holding a pillow in my lap.

"Do you want to talk about it, Lacey?" the group leader asks, the one with the clipboard. Everyone else is doing their own thing. A few us look like we are listening. Others doze off from the meds they're on. I haven't been put on any yet. That's one of my biggest fears but I don't think I have any control over it. After all, this is just my first day.

"I hate it when my Mom comes. She always talks about herself. She said I only have a few days left here because of the insurance so I better get cured in the last few days that I'm here."

The leader asks, "Are you scared to go home? Some of us get scared when it's time to

back home and face our demons." *Interesting* I
thought as I shift positions on the couch, trying to
pay attention but I can't sit still.

"A little. I'll just wait to talk with Dr.
Ruby." Lacey shuts down.

"Ok, ladies, remember to breath, and
don't forget to write in your journals. Chantel,
will you stay for a minute. You get to see Dr.
Ruby," the group leader - her name is Kristy -
says as the other girls walk out single file and go
on with their day. According to the brochure that
I got in the packet, there are several different
groups and therapy, all individualized for each
case.

I walk next to Kristy as she takes me to
see Dr. Ruby. She keeps talking about who she is
and what she does here. There are different
positions that all the staff play. Kristy is a group
leader who specializes in behavior management.
She seems nice. She has a teenage daughter and a
son who's in kindergarten. Not that that matters.
Just part of the bits in pieces of information that I
catch while listening.

"Here we are. This is Dr. Ruby's office."
There's some type of fan that's sitting outside the
corner of the door of the office. Kristy says it's
for privacy, so that if anyone walks by the door,

no one can hear what's being said. I wonder if people can hear tears.

"Hello, Dr. Ruby. This is Chantel." This large black woman with old lady red glasses answers the door and reaches out to shake my hand.

"Hello, Chantel. Thanks, Kristy. I have it from here. Hi, Chantel. Why don't you have a seat over there." She points to a black leather chair in a corner next to the window. From what I can gather, it's the only window I've seen without bars on it.

"Hello," I say back.

"So, Chantel, tell me, what brings you here?"

"The school and my parents put me here," I say with an angry tone.

"No, you put yourself here."

"Oh, sure, I want to spend my Saturday afternoon in a loony bin with a bunch of crazy girls."

"What I meant was your behavior got you here, honey. Want to tell me what that was?" She leans forwards and tries to make eye contact with me.

"I've been cutting myself," I say while swallowing a big lump in my throat.

"I'm sorry you're having to go through this. There are many different reasons and theories about why people, especially young girls, do this. It's more common than you probably think." She keeps talking about cutting and introduces me to the idea of new medications. Medications for me would be a first. My mom has trouble getting me to take regular Tylenol.

I kept staring at the clock on Dr. Ruby's wall. I know when the hour has ended. The end of our session. I have to see Dr. Ruby twice a week while I'm here. I don't know how long I'm going to be here, but I know for a week at least. Funny thing is, I don't want to go home. I actually feel content here. I mean, I don't have access to my cell phone or any electronics, but that doesn't bother me. There is no one laying out my clothes on my bed. No one tells me I look like shit each day. I know, right? This came from my dad. He once told me that I was too ugly to look at when he picked me up from school. He made me sit down on the car floor. For the first time, I feel free. I'm scared. I don't know what the hell I'm supposed to do with all this.

Chapter 3
The Therapist

The black leather couch. The talking back and forth. Prescribing patient medications. The clock on the wall. The fancy nameplate on the desk. All the certificates on the wall behind the chair. On her desk are pictures of what looks like a happy family. Pictures worth a thousand words. What if the picture is ripped? What if there's a line down the middle? What really happens behind closed doors?

Every five years our church puts together a "church family" photo album of all the families and members of the church. The list is called a directory. In the back of the directory, people's names are listed in alphabetical order with their phone numbers and emails. And their birthdates, too. Every year the elder of the church sends out birthday cards. As a child, church services were some of the happiest memories of my childhood. I was involved in children's choir and youth group programs. Not so much as an adult. Not sure why this memory came up. Funny how a single picture can bring up something from the past. Doesn't matter if it's happy or sad, or from long ago or now.

"Hello." This lady is standing in my room folding clothes. I had not seen her before.

"Hello. Who are you?" I ask, trying not to sound rude. Why is a strange lady folding clothes in my room?

"I see you two have met each other." Nurse June comes in with a bubbly voice.

"No, we were just getting to that.'

"Great. Chantel, this is Lana. Lana, this is Chantel. Chantel, Lana is your new roommate. Chantel, you have Dr. Ruby in ten minutes. I'll let you get ready." Nurse June walks away. This is awkward. I've never had a roommate before. Even at home my sister and younger brother and I have always had our own room.

"Hi, Chantel. How old are you, honey? You look so young," Lana says as she continues to put her clothes away like she knew what she was doing. Or at least had done it before.

"How old are YOU?" I snap back, feeling a bit frustrated because I got a roommate.

"A lady never reveals her true age. You just look so young. At your age what could be so painful for you to be in a place like this?" I don't answer back. I'm still too pissed that I got a roommate. So I sit on my bed and wait for Nurse June.

I like being by myself. I always have. Guess because I feel different then everyone else around me. I see people at school hanging out at lunch time with all their friends, groupies, taking pictures. The sounds of laugher trailing in the hallways. I have a few friends but we don't talk a lot. But in some ways we are there for each other.

Lucy was my first friend who found out I was a cutter. I had just failed my math test so I went into the bathroom at school and I cut my wrist and ran it underneath the toilet paper dispenser. It's hard to use my cat as an excuse. What kind of cat leaves scratches in perfect little lines like that? Or little specks or pokes.

"How are you feeling today, Chantel?" Dr. Ruby asks me as she pulls out the clipboard. I wish I could look at that clipboard. I wonder what she keeps on it. I know there's a notepad. Why does she keep notes of what I say? Probably because I'm not her only patient. I wonder how many patients she sees in a day. I wonder, with this type of job, if the therapist has to see a therapist? I bet it would get pretty depressing seeing crazy people hour after hour five days a week. I just wonder sometimes what the doctors' lives are like at home. Where do they go when they leave here? Do we go with them inside their heads? Do they really care about us patients or do we just give them a paycheck?

"I'm okay. Just a little pissed about getting a roommate. I wasn't ready for that," I say, dangling my leg across the other leg and my hands folded.

"Thank you for being honest with me. Why are you pissed about having a roommate?" Dr. Ruby asks as she gets that fancy pen ready.

"I like having my own room. My own privacy. I think that's the only thing I really miss being in here," I said as I look toward the ground."

"You don't miss your family?"

"No, not really.

"That didn't take you long to answer. Tell me about your family."

"Why?"

"Well, I'm just trying to get a little background information about you. See where we can begin working on some tools and figure out what brought you to us." She generally seems caring.

How do I tell the therapist what's going on when I can't? How do I tell the therapist that what's really bothering me lives in my house just down the hallway from my bedroom. I think that's why I've always liked a corner space. My bed at home is set up against the furthest corner away from the door, with my favorite purple comforter with flowers on it. My kitty Leon likes to sleep on top of my head. He's a big fat fluffy black cat. I got him for Christmas when he was just a baby. My mom had set him underneath the Christmas tree with a little red bow on top. I wanted to name him Sparky. Sparky used to be Grandma's cat's name. But dad came up with Leon. I guess when he was a kid, he got a kitten for Christmas and had a Christmas decoration in tin cans that spelled Noel and Noel spelled backwards is Leon. Dad always has a sense of humor. He can be charming, witty. Full of life. The perfect family man. 'Till he drinks. Then his secrets come out to play. But I'm the crazy one. I must be because I am here for cutting on myself and he's not here.

"Lunch time in ten minutes." The intercom voice comes on again. Sounds like one of those creepy female voices from a scary movie. At least that's what it reminds me of. Time to line up and walk in a straight line. Every meal. Every room.

"Chantel, are you settled in?" Becca asks as she pulls up a tray and sits next to me.

"I guess. I saw Dr. Ruby. She seems ok."

"Yeah, she's cool. So far she seems to be the only person who hasn't pissed me off."

"Becca, I'm offended. See you in group and eat your apple," Nurse Mary says with a chuckle.

"You know how many calories are in an apple?" *Really? A frickin' apple? Who cares,* I think to myself. Becca must be a food issue patient. I never heard a normal eater complain about how many calories are in an apple.

"Fucking 52 calories! Might as well throw in the whip cream." Laughter from the other girls sitting at the table.

"Becca, do you want to pick the movie for tonight?" Nurse Mary tries to distract her.

"Hmmmm... make Chantel do it."

"Wait! What movie?"

"On Friday nights the girls on the ward, if they have their level two privileges, get to watch a movie in the girls' day room."

"Sorry, Chantel," says Nurse Mary. "You can't pick the movie." I don't really want to watch it anyway. I'd rather sleep. Sleep is one of my favorite past times. You know, I actually sleep more here than at home. The first couple of nights I couldn't sleep. Between the nurse coming in every ten minutes doing bed checks, and me keeping an eye out on the door for dad to come in. He hasn't been in my room for three days now. I wonder if he goes into my room at home while I'm here? I hope Leon doesn't get lonely.

Dad comes in my room at night. Our little secret, he calls it. He brings cookies and milk. Oreos because they're my favorite. I used to like to take the cookie and lick the cream off then put the cookies back together and put them back into the cookie jar. Grandma would get so mad. The last couple of years dad ruined my love of Oreo cookies. He does something different with the cream than licking it off the cookie.

At night I can tell that it's not the same bedroom as at home. Not just because dad doesn't come into my room. When the lights go out here, it seems like a whole other planet. You can hear all the sounds of everyone's tears. Everyone's screams. Funny, even though some of us are on heavy duty medications, we still wake up screaming. I wonder if we all have the same nightmares. Some of us hallucinate. Some sit up and rock back and forth in our beds. Rocking back and forth is soothing. My Mom gets so pissed off when I sit in public, like a church pew, and rock my body back and forth. But my anxiety gets so high that all I can do is rock. Especially if I can't get to something sharp.

"Breakfast in ten minutes." Looks like I made it through another night. All the girls have several group therapies throughout the day. From art therapy to gymnastics. It all depends on what we're in here for.

"Hi, ladies. How did the weekend go?" Nurse Kristy is back. Must be Monday. I've lost track. But we don't have groups on the weekend. Just more gym time and art classes and stuff like that. And I always have Dr. Ruby after group.

"Good. We have a new patient joining us," Julie says.

"Yeah, Grandma Moses," Amber blurts out.

"Now girls. All ages are welcomed in this facility. That's why it's called a Women's Residential Treatment facility." Something tells me that this is a smaller type of hospital. Like the prevention before they ship people off to the next higher up hospital.

The counselor and I meet again. I like the chair. The good leather chair. It has marble at the end and some old polyester material. I like to pick at the strings that are starting to pull apart.

"Tell me about your cutting," Dr. Ruby says. Today she chose a different chair. This one is a little closer to the chair I am sitting on.

"What do you want to know?" Answer a question with a question.

"Why do you think you do it? What do you use?" Dr. Ruby asks. Nobody's ever flat out asked me those questions before. Not sure how honest she wants me to be. I feel like I need my dad's permission to tell her that.

"I cut because I can't feel anything when I cut. Like, the whole world just disappears."

"What don't you want to feel?" My heart races, about to pop out of my chest. *Just say it* as I try to force my mouth open to speak the words.

"My dad."

Chapter 4
Discharged

A blade, a pair of scissors, or my recent favorite, broken glass. Dr. Ruby wants me to write in my journal about my cutting and why I do it, then bring it to the next therapy session. I've never thought about it before. I've been doing it for so long that I can't remember the first time I did it.

My favorite place to cut? Environment, that is. My bathroom, in the tub, I think, because after I'm done cutting, the water washes it all away. Somehow, watching the blood circle down the drain is soothing. When I cut, I disappear. Like an out-of-body experience, watching my body go down the drain. When I cut, my feelings go away. I feel dirty, ashamed, sad, bad. It's funny, well, until I got here, I couldn't name any feelings other than sad or mad. I know what happy is, but I haven't experienced it in a long time. When I *have* laughed, most of the time it's because I'm so uncomfortable that the only thing I can do is laugh or make other people around me laugh so they don't worry about me.

I miss my kitty. He would come lay on the bed with me. If I was having a good day or a bad day, especially if I had a bad day, he would rub up against me until I finally gave him attention. That would usually distract me from crying.

When the blade or sharp object touches my skin, I drag it up and down my arms. The blood comes out and I'm free. I cut in all sorts of places. Wrists, legs. Recently, before coming in here, it was my breasts. Why I'm not really sure. For me cutting isn't a suicide attempt. It's a coping mechanism. From what I've heard, there are many forms of self-injury. Some people cut, some people bang their heads up against the wall over and over to calm themselves down. Some people burn their own skin to the point that it scars. I kind of know how that feels.

One night, after my dad came into my room, I was so angry that I threw myself down on the floor and just cried 'till I fell asleep. Next day I sat in the bathtub and took a hot shower. As hot as it could be. I don't even think I felt the temperature of the water. I just wanted him out of me.

"Why are you crying, Lana?" I ask as I catch her on her bed.

"Oh, it's nothing, dear." She wipes her nose with an ugly green sweatshirt sleeve.

"Obviously it's something. I can see you're upset."

"My son came for visitors' day today."

"That didn't go well?"

"It went okay. He's just so angry that I'm here. He's disappointed in me as a mother."

I don't know what to say so I listen. I'm not a mom so I don't know how to help her. I mean, I can only imagine what my mom must think of me being in here. I wonder what she's telling everyone back home. Especially the church.

My dad's an elder in the church. Mom sings in the church choir. My sister Emma is involved in Sunday school. It's amazing to me how you can make the outsides look good. Perfect clothes, perfect family. Some days I feel like I'm in a crowded room, screaming at the top of my lungs but no one looks up. No one knows what's happening at home. Behind closed doors. Why would they? Don't ask, don't tell, right? Black eye, bruise on the arm? Just cover it up with a little purple eyeshadow and mascara. If the bruise was on the arm, a little foundation to cover it up. God, I can only imagine what my mother's hiding. I've got my personal hell. What kind of war does she have? Does he touch her anymore? Why did he choose me?

It's funny, adults say, that children can't remember much. My parents fought all the time. When we were younger, I used to make my sister

Emma come in my room with me. I would play loud music. That way, when dad yelled at mom, Emma couldn't hear it. I wanted to keep Emma as quiet as we could be. That way he wouldn't hurt her, too.

"Art therapy in ten minutes." I love art. My favorite classes at school are art and choir. Both music and art have different forms of expression. My choir teacher, Mr. Jones, was also our drivers ed teacher. My friend Jenna was a year older than me. She was taking drivers ed and would tell me some of the funny stories from Mr. Jones. Apparently, if you ran a stop sign while driving the student drivers ed car, he would make you get out and hug the stop sign and apologize to it.

"Today's art project, tree of feelings." Laughter from some of the girls. I was a little nervous. In the art room there's a bunch of different plastic containers with locks. On the walls was art from previous patients that were here. There's glue, crayons, markers, colored pencils, and construction paper. I wonder what damage could be done with crayon? Never mind. I don't want to think about it. Sometimes I forget where I am. As we start to draw, I find that I like to use the oil pastels. I like the feeling of when I touch the paper. Somehow I disappear into it. I like that feeling.

"Becca, look at Lana's tree." Laughter from Julie.

"What's so damn funny?" Lana snaps back. I feel bad for her.

"It's in black and white." Julie points out to everyone.

"Girls, what's the big fuss over here?" Paula the art therapist comes over to see what is happening.

"Lana drew her tree in black and white."

"Instead of laughing at Lana, why don't you ask her why she chose to draw in black and white. I never said you had to use color. I just said the objective of the assignment was to draw a tree with feelings. Trees come in many shapes and sizes. Good job, Lana. Do you want to share why you drew your tree black and white?" Paula asks.

"I can't feel anything. I feel like I'm the leaves that fall off the branches when they are dead and fall to the ground." The room got silent.

"Can I share this with Dr. Ruby?" Paula asks with one of those fake smiles trying to cover up the concerned look on her face.

Why is it so hard to express feelings? Why is it not socially acceptable to cry? I tried to cry when Lana talked about the way she felt with the drawing. Nothing could come out. We were seen, not heard. We always had to look our best. We don't talk about it. We suck it up and do it any way. Damn, I wish I could cut. I'm feeling and I don't like it. I'm scared.

"Chantel, in ten minutes. Don't forget to bring your journal." My heart races a million miles a minute. I hope she won't read it. Mom did that once. I wrote in my journal about how suicidal I felt a couple years ago. When I came home from school, there my journal sat, flopped open. My family's pastor was sitting there. I was so pissed, especially since I had a note on the front of the journal that said in big letters KEEP OUT AND THAT MEANS YOU! Maybe that was an invitation. A cry for help. But how could I speak about what was really bothering me when the person that was bothering me was in my house?

Chapter 5
Family Day

"Do you have anyone coming for family day?" Lana asks me as we are getting ready to head down to the cafeteria.

"Yes, my mom's coming," I say in a low voice.

"You almost sound disappointed?" Lana sort of asks.

"Not really. I'm just nervous. My family is very religious, and sometimes judgmental, because of things they don't understand."

"I know the feeling. My son can't stand the ground I walk on. I tried the best I could to raise him. After his father cheated on me I couldn't stand to stay married to him. I was much better off making the choice to leave. But Cody's never let me forget that I divorced his dad."

In some families there are the usual secrets. Then there are secrets that go deeper than blood. When the truth is set free, the family splits up and decides which side to take. No matter what our personal hell is, it's all about show and tell. Even if it's made up. It's been two weeks since I haven't had any contact with my dad. It's an unsettling feeling. You'd think that being away from him, I'd feel freedom. Oddly enough, it's just the opposite. I feel bound by invisible chains. He's the voice in my head. He rules my day and haunts my sleep. I wonder if he's sleeping while I'm gone. I wonder what he's thinking.

"Group therapy in ten minutes." The famous intercom speaks again. Going on almost two weeks since I first checked in. Starting to get the routine. Dr. Ruby and I check in once a day. I'm starting to write in my journal more. Before I came here, I never knew how to journal. Nor was it interesting to me. I actually have grown quite fond of the idea, especially now that I know I'm in a safe place. I haven't been able to write in a journal since my mom snuck in my room and had the pastor come over.

"Are you ready for group, kid?" Kid? How strange for Lana to call me kid. Maybe because she's fifty-five and I'm fifteen? Maybe I'm a comfort to her somehow. *Just roll with it,* Lucy would say.

"Yeah. Are you?" I reply back.

"Now or never, right?" Lana said as she takes a deep breath and puts on her stringless purple sweatshirt.

We walk together to the group room. Now that I have privileges, I have a little more freedom than when I first got here. Except when we leave the building. We're all escorted.

"Good morning, girls. How is everyone this morning?" I can't get over the enthusiasm of the workers here. Of *course* they would be. They're not spending long nights in here, hearing all the awful cries and sounds of the middle of the night.

"Good morning," we all respond.

"Anybody have anything they'd like to talk about this morning?"

"Whoever's peeing in the shower, can you please stop?" Jonna speaks up.

"Why? It's a a great way to kill athletes foot!" says Krista, the group counselor

"Did she really just say that?" Laughter from the other girls.

"Are we ready for family day? Who's got visitors today?"

According to some of the other patients here, a lot of them don't always have visitors or family that comes to see them. A lot of them are court ordered here. That's why this place is locked down with such tight security. I think that's why they say I'm one of the "lucky ones."

"Visiting hours starts in ten minutes." The famous intercom always gives the ward a ten-minute warning before each group starts.

Those who don't have visitors get to have free time or to enjoy a craft project in the art room.

"Hi, Baby." Mom sees me as she walks up to me with her arms wide open. I hug her in return.

"I didn't realize it would be like visiting someone in prison coming to see you. I had to go through a metal detector and have my purse checked." *Nice to see you, too, Mom*, I thought to myself as she rambled on and on about herself.

"How are you doing in this thing?" Mom asks as she puts on some lip gloss. Wish I could have some. This "thing" is a psychiatric hospital. She can't even say it. Some days I wonder if it would have been easier on her if I had succeeded in killing myself. I wish I did. I've tried several times. I guess maybe I'm just too chicken-shit to off myself. There was a kid in my freshman year of high school. His name was Dylan. He hung himself in his garage. The students at the school were mostly devastated. I remember because they had to have extra counselors come in for the funeral and to help the students deal with their emotions at school.

"Ok, I guess. They keep us busy."

"Yeah? What do you do?"

"Well, we have group therapy several times a day. And we see a counselor daily."

"That's good. I hope you're getting something beneficial here. After all, my insurance is paying for this. This thing that you do."

This thing I do? Mom doesn't get it. She thinks I'm here on some vacation day at the spa. I wish that's what it was. It's so much more than a vacation. I'm literally trying to save my life. That's what the counselors and nursing staff in groups try to emphasize.

Chapter 6
Forms of
Communication

"Have you ever been so depressed that you just want to die? Most days I don't even want to get out of bed."

"Why do you want to die, Chantel?" the therapist asks me. A brief pause. All I can do is stare off into space. "Chantel, that's a powerful statement. You want to die?" the therapist asks in a caring voice as she leans over.

"I know. I just want it to end. But I don't know how to talk about it." How do I tell her? How do I tell her what's going on between dad and me? She'll think I'm some kind of freak or something. I feel like a freak. I feel so dirty and confused. He's my dad. Just tell her. Why can't I just tell her? I want to tell her. But I can't.

"Wanting it to end is a pretty strong statement. If you can't say it, can you write about it?" The therapist begins to explain to me that there are several ways to communicate, not just through words. There is art, writing, music and dance. I'm pretty sure I can't dance to express it.

"Okay, I'll write it." After I say that, I take a deep sigh as she hands me her note pad.

"I want to remind you that this is a safe place, Chantel. Nobody can hurt you here, okay, sweetie?" The therapist tries to reassure me that I'm safe. *As long as I'm in here,* I thought to myself. *If I go home, I'm not.*

I stare at the notepad then stare at the therapist. She hands me a pen as I sit. My body shakes. *He never said I couldn't write about it. He just said I couldn't tell anyone about it. This should be okay, right?*

It takes me fifteen minutes to write three letters. I just freeze.

"Chantel, are you with me? Chantel?" I freeze and stare. I can hear her but I can't respond. I want to, but I can't move.

"Chantel, blink once if you can me hear the sound of my voice." I blink once.

"Good girl. Now I want you to take your hand and feel the couch that you're sitting on. Can you do that for me?" I feel the couch. It's nice and soft. I start to move my fingers. I'm coming back.

"I'm done for today," I say, about ready to leap towards the door.

"Good job today, Chantel," the therapist says. The nurse comes in to take me back.

"How are you doing today? You look a lot better than the last time I saw you in here," Nurse Christa says as she walks me back to the unit. I don't answer her. My head is still in the therapy room in all honesty. I'm still in shock.

I get back to my room and all I want to do is sleep. I feel like I haven't slept in days. Secrets keep us sick. Secrets cause health problems. Depression, fibromyalgia, autoimmune diseases. The body has powerful ways of protecting itself according to the counselor. She told me that I'd be tired, that it is okay to sleep if I want to.

"What movie do we want to watch tonight?" Becca asks as she takes a bite of what looks like a peanut butter and jelly sandwich. I really don't care about the movie. I still feel frozen.

"Hey, Chantel. Have you gotten it yet?" *Got what,* I think to myself as I stay silent and stare at her.

"The med doc?" The other girls start laughing.

"Yes." I say.

"Well, that explains the stare."

"Shut up, Becca," I shout back.

"What's going on over here, girls?" One of the nurses hears me yell.

"Becca keeps making fun of me."

"Ok, girls, cut it out. Becca, you get written up. Group in ten minutes."

Oh shit, I think. I know I'm in trouble. Becca is a big girl. She has half of her head shaved and the other side long. I think she had a bunch of piercings because of how her face looks, but when you come here you can't have any piercings because of the sharpness of the earrings.

"Becca, why are you so mad with Chantel?"

"Because she never says anything. She just sits and participates but doesn't share a single word."

"Well, Becca, if you weren't such a bitch and absorbed in yourself, maybe you would get to know her," Lana snaps back. I pull my legs up onto the couch and start rocking my body back and forth.

"Exhibit A. See? We're talking about her and she still says nothing."

"Actually, Becca, by Chantel rocking the way she is and not saying anything is a way of communication. The body language of people can tell many different things. Signs of trouble, signs of happiness. It's just their way of being able to express and communicate. Why does her behavior irritate you?"

"I don't know," Becca says in a quiet voice with almost a stare.

"Even right there, what you just said and did, exhibits an underlying response."

I'm about to pull my hair out. I can't take this anymore. I wonder if the nurse can up my meds. I wonder if there is a combination so strong that I can just zone out for the rest of my life. Why am I here? Why am I alive? What am I supposed to do now? I'm a pain in the ass everywhere I go. I can't even get along with girls in a nut house. That's a special kind of special.

Chapter 7
The Hard Question

Did you know that child abuse affects more people than cancer? Scary thought, right? I wonder how many people actually come out and tell people that they have been raped by their fathers for years and years? It seems so taboo because, well, it is. I don't like that word incest. (Webster definition: sexual intercourse between persons so closely related that they are forbidden by law to marry; a statuary crime). Basically, sexual relations between father and daughter. Why does it have to be called incest or inbreeding?

Rape has its own frightening demeanor. You go through the normal feelings of shame, guilt, dirty. You think that it's your fault no matter what people tell you. I cannot think about it that way. Was I wearing something that provoked it? Why me? What was so special about me? I freeze. Is it still rape if I freeze and let him do it? He didn't mean to, he said. He was drunk. Why do we blame ourselves when it's the other person's fault? Of course all the professionals tell me it's nothing I did. A small part of me knows that somewhere. But for the amount of times that it happened, how do I know it isn't my fault? Professionals say that freeze is a normal response. It's somehow the body's way of shutting down and protecting itself.

Is it still considered child abuse when you're thirteen? Fourteen? Fifteen? Does that mean I wanted it? I haven't been able to tell anybody so does that mean it's my fault because it keeps happening? How do I tell my mom that I'm being raped over and over almost every night by my own father? If it were stranger rape, the family would be more supportive, I think.

According to some of the girls in here who have shared their stories, their families were horrible after coming out with the truth. They choose sides, they blame the victim, they call them liars if they don't believe them. I wanna know...why would we make these horrible accusations if it didn't happen? It's nearly impossible for people who have been raped to be heard.

"Good luck with your appointment, Chantel," Lana says as she is drawing on a notepad sitting on her bed.

"Um, thanks. You've never said that before a session before."

"So?" Lana snaps.

"Well, why would you say that to me now?" I ask out of curiosity.

"You talk in your sleep."

"Ready?" Nurse Christa comes to the door. I grab my journal and march on to the shrink's office. What did I say in my sleep? I had no idea I talk in my sleep. I don't have any roommates at home, so how would I know that? What the hell did I say in my sleep?

Have you ever had nightmares so bad that they feel like they have just happened to you when you wake up? I guess it's normal to have nightmares when you're a little kid. Even when you're an adult, it's okay. But is it normal to wake up to your own urination in your bed from screaming in a dream?

"Hi, Chantel. How you doing, honey?" the therapist asks. She asks me if she can sit in a different chair that's a little closer to me than before. Now I'm really scared.

"Sure." I say as my heart feels like it's going to pound out of my chest.

"How are you feeling today?" she asks as she dates the top of the page of her notepad.

"I'm okay," I say, picking at the marble again.

"Can you use any other word than okay?" the therapist asks, handing me a piece of paper with a list of words. *Okay* is at the top of the page. Underneath in brackets are other words that might be suitable for the word *okay*. According to the therapist, *ok* and *fine* are words that people use when they don't really want to express or share how they are really feeling.

"Sad, I think." Sad is one of the feeling words on the list.

"Why are you sad? Are you sad about what you wrote on the paper last time?" the therapist asks. I shake my head.

"Chantel, I'm going to ask you a question. Is that ok?" My heart starts racing. Tears come.

"Okay," I say in a quiet tone.

"Is your dad raping you on a daily basis at home?"

I couldn't move. Then I threw up in the trash can.

Chapter 8
Diagnosis

Being in this place has its advantages and disadvantages. I miss my privacy, especially the times he didn't come into my room.

You get to know the sounds of people's screams, people's tears. Nighttime is just a whole other planet. Even with all the medications that we're all on, nighttime is a different battleground. I mean, think about it: when you wake up in the middle of the night you're already disoriented. Then you're put into a strange place that's unfamiliar. You wake up to a different environment with bars on the windows.

"Good morning," Lana says to me, all spunky and refreshed from getting out of the shower. Did you know we can't even shower by ourselves? We have to have a nurse stay with us in the shower room. Like, what are we going to do? Strangle ourselves with the shower curtain?

I hate the medications I'm on. I feel so calm and spacey. I don't know how to handle it. They diagnosed me with Post Traumatic Stress Disorder (PTSD) and depression. My mother will be thrilled to hear this, with her perfect little world and church-going family. Except for me who doesn't fit in. My parents are coming to meet the therapist today and have a family session. Not sure how to feel or what to think. I think I'm more scared of my father's reaction rather than my mom's.

One of the questions I have is to know why I have PTSD. What is it? I've only heard of war veterans coming back from war and getting diagnosed with PTSD. But I guess it's not just about war victims anymore. Women and men who have had something traumatic happen to them seem to get it, like a car accident, witnessing a crime, abusive rela-tionhip. I was scared getting this diagnosis because that means people are starting to listen, and I haven't told them what exactly happened. The only thing I like about the group therapy is that I'm learning that it hap-pens to more people than I thought. I haven't shared in group yet. But I'm starting to trust the workers here and to accept their help. They say accepting is the first step in healing.

"Hey, Lana, do you have anybody coming for visitors' day today?" I ask.

"No, but that's okay. I'm going to take a nap." I'm worried by her response. She seems a little more upbeat than usual. I don't know. Maybe her therapy is going good.

"How long have you been in here, Lana?" I ask out of courtesy. I will have been here for three weeks on Saturday. I'm starting to earn some of my privileges for good behavior. That's why I get my first family visit.

"My parents are coming today," I say in a quiet voice.

"How do you feel about that?" Lana asks me. Until I came here, no one ever asked me how I feel about anything. I'm not used to all the compassion and kindness of adults or anyone for that matter.

I'm scared. Mostly of seeing my dad. And my mom won't be too thrilled, either. I can handle her but I don't know how to handle my dad. I wonder if he knows I'm afraid of him? I wonder if he's afraid of being around me? Being in this hospital has been the longest I've ever been away from either of my parents

"Hi, I'm the counselor here at the recovery center. You must be Mr. and Mrs. Brown?" the therapist asks while shaking their hands.

"Yes, we are. Pleased to meet you. Thank you for helping our daughter. We sure do miss her at home and can't wait to have her back with us," my mother says as she grabs a Kleenex from her purse.

"So how much longer does my daughter have to be in here?" my dad bluntly asks.

"Well, sir, it depends on how she reponds to treatment. I'm diagnosing your daughter with depression and PTSD," the therapist says.

"Oh, my girl isn't depressed. If she is, it's because she's in here. Hell, I'm depressed just looking at the color of the paint on the walls and this horrible carpet."

"So what is this PTSD business?" my dad asks. Mother just sits there.

Wow! I can't believe my parents' response. I just sit there listening and watching. Gotta get back to my room.

"Help!!! Help !!!!" I scream! When I do get back to the room, Lana is passed out on the floor with a towel around her neck.

The staff quickly sends everyone to a different wing and I get sent to a private observation room. I feel frozen, scared. I just talked to Lana before my therapy session. She could have reached out to me. I would have listened. Why did she have to kill herself?

Chapter 9
Discharged

When most people hear about self-injury or cutting, they often know myths, not facts. The big myth, that cutting is a suicide attempt, is not a fact. Cutting is a coping mechanism. A cry for help.

One night I wanted to cut so bad but I fought it. I rocked hard back and forth. Then I literally picked up my body and threw myself to the floor. Oddly enough, I felt better. The urge went away.

People often don't know how to support loved ones who cut. It took a long time for my mom to come around.

My father was never put in jail because I never had the guts or the courage to turn him in. I was too scared to tell my family and my friends. He had a lot of power in my community with police authority and his old job.

I wish I could have had the courage back then to allow my teachers to help me when they started to question me. I guess it isn't normal for a student to walk into her counselor's office and ask to take a shower. The next day my father walked into her office and said I was making all this up and was just wanting attention. Shortly after that I was put in the hospital.

To this day my mom doesn't know all the details of what happens to me. What she does know, she, or at least her actions, show that she has a rough time understanding what hell I've really been through. No one needs that in their head. I do know that with professional help, family support, and sometimes medication, I can heal. Everybody has their own path. No two people are alike, even if it's the same event.

I cut to cope with the abuse that has gone on in my life. One day I hope to give back to my community the way I've been helped. With the right professional help and time, healing is possible. Not easy!! But possible.

My dad and I rarely speak. He doesn't understand why we don't have a good relationship today. He tells my brothers and sisers a completely different story from what actually happened between us.

I'm still in therapy and living life as normally as I can. After all, normal is just a setting on the dryer.

I watched Lana's family come into our room and gather her things. I watched her daughter pack things up and head out the door. It was almost like she was relieved. I don't want Lana's death to be in vain. In some ways, her death helped me find my voice. It's funny, up until Lana's death, I never wanted to live. I was always so jealous of people when they could off themselves. I always feared that I would do it wrong. Then there was the whole fear of going to hell which I heard from the church I was raised in. They taught me the consequences of what killing myself would look like in eternity.

If you cut, seek help. Tell someone as soon as you can. Secrets keep us sick. It's their shame, not ours. One day the rapists and abusers will have to meet their maker. I'm choosing to move on with my life, not because the pain is gone, but because it's the best gift I can give myself, to live happy. Don't ever let anyone steal your joy. Keep your head held high. Remember, you're not alone. There are millions of people around the world who have been through what we've been through. We've all coped in different ways. Take back your power. Put down the knife. Don't bleed for them today. Choose hope.

54

Resources

Alcoholics Anonymous
https://www.aa.org

National Sexual Assault Hotline
1.800.656 HOPE

National Suicide Prevention Lifeline
1-800-273-TALK (1-800-273-8255)
suicidepreventionlifeline.org/chat

Rape, Abuse, and Incest National Network
(RAININ)
1.800.656.4673
Www.selfinjury.com

Self Alternatives information line
1.800.dontcut

24 hour Self-Harm Crisis Text
741-741

Articles/Books

How to Parent a Teen That Self Harms
https://www.psycom.net/parent-a-teen-that-self-harms/

When Your Child Is Cutting: A Parents Guide to Helping Children Overcome Self Injury by McEvey-Noble, M.E., Khemlani-Patel, S., & F. Neziroglu. (2006). New Harbinger Publications

Stopping the Pain: A Workbook for Teens Who Cut & Self-Injure by Lawrence E. Shapiro (2008) Instant Help Books

Made in the USA
Coppell, TX
03 August 2021

59884220R00039